Illustrated by Jill Newton

Orlando Boston Dallas Chicago San Diego

Printed in the United States of America

ISBN 0-15-314981-7

4 5 6 7 8 9 10 026 2001 2000

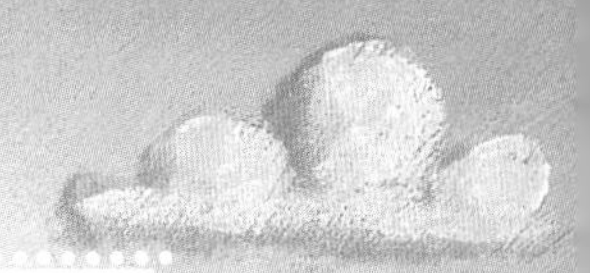

CONTENTS

Where Is Sam?

Where is Sam?

Sam.

Sam?

Sam!

Here I am.

I am Sam.

# Sam Sat

Look at that mat.

Sam sat.

Look at that mat.

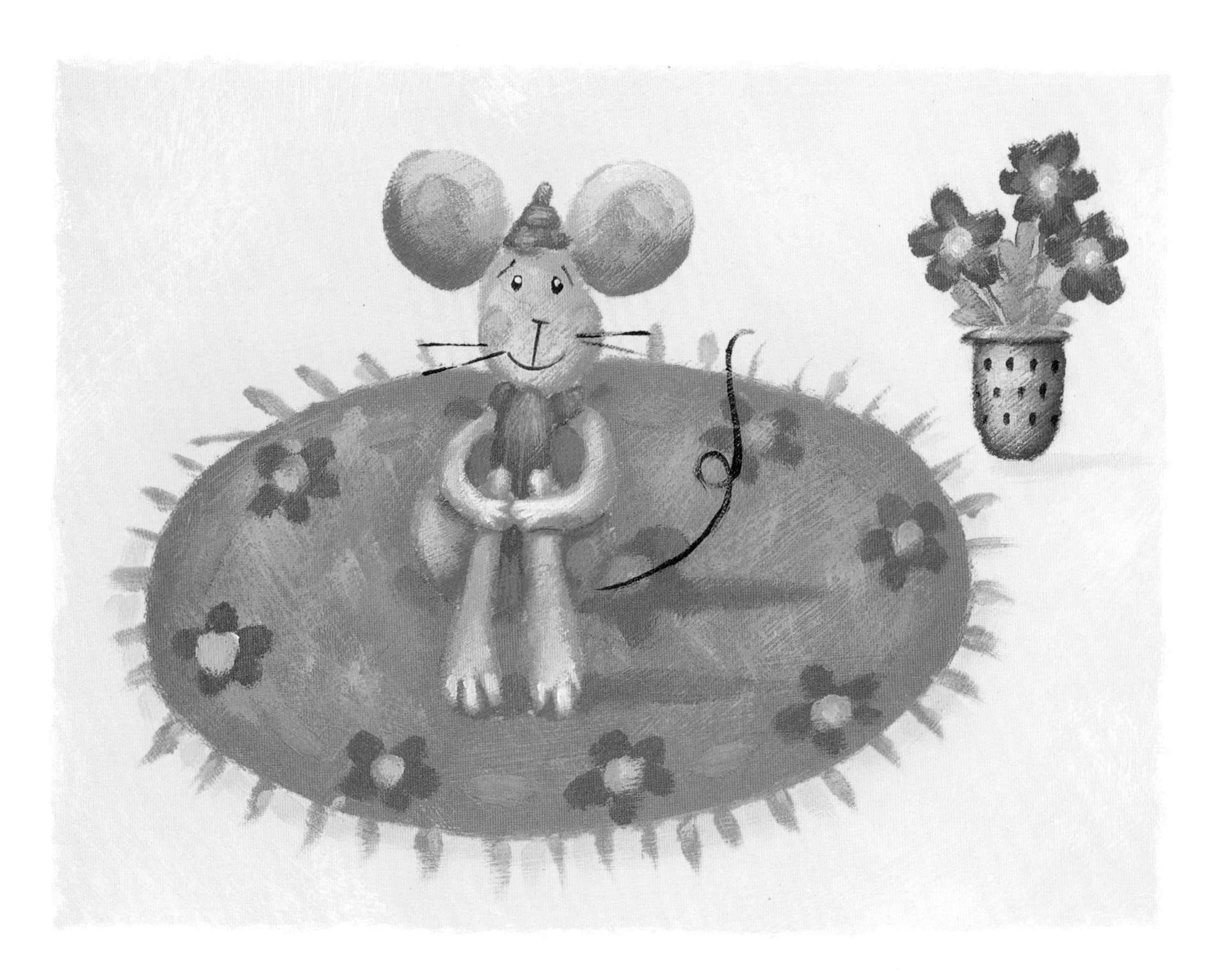

Sam sat.

Look at that cat!

Sam sat.

MEOW!

# Come Here, Cat

Cat. Cat.

Come here, Cat.

Cat. Cat.

I am here cat!

Cat. Cat.

Look at me!